BLUE GOLD
THE TURQUOISE STORY

BY M. G. BROMAN

●

Library Congress
Catalog Card Number
74-20148

Published
by
Main Street Press
P.O. Box 4262
Anaheim, California
92803

Distributed
by
Gem Guides Book Co.
5409 Lenvale
Whittier, Calif. 90601

Acknowledgements

The author wishes to acknowledge the kind assistance of the following people who were instrumental in furnishing data for this publication.

Kathy Mayerski
Title — Blue Gold

Alfred Mayerski
Research and Source Assistance

Sandy Broman
Art and assistance with writing

Debbie and Mike Gurganious
Map, photography, models

Gordon and Priscilla Williams
Assistant set-up

Senator Barry Goldwater
Phoenix, Arizona

Stuart A. Northrop
Research Professor Emeritus of Geology
University of New Mexico

Fritz Wright
Jewelsmith
Handcrafted, Custom
Turquoise Jewelry
P.O. 5863 Orange, California 92667

Bob and Rita Mortan
Treasure Trails Inc.
Disneyland Hotel Plaza
1441 S. West Street
Anaheim, California 92802

O.F. De Castro
Indian Trader
Turquoise Teepee
3412 Via Oparto, Lido Village
Newport Beach, California 92660

Ray and Fay Feaster
Hozuna Traders
12138 Brookhurst
Garden Grove, California 92604

Jeff Kurtzeman
Photographer
3048 East Lufsine Avenue
Phoenix, Arizona 85028

Mr. Carol Ennis
Photographer
1529 East Elm Street
Anaheim, California 92805

Ray Manley
Commercial Photography
238 South Tucson Blvd.
Tucson, Arizona 85716

Arizona Highways Office Staff

John Macdonald
General Manager of
Hozuna Traders
Earth Trading Unlimited
12138 Brookhurst
Garden Grove, California 92640

Dedication

This book is dedicated to my children Debbie, Mike, Sandy, Mike, Edna, & Pat who did nothing to interfere with the creation of this book, and Harold too.

INTRODUCTION

Photo Compliments of Senator Barry Goldwater

This simply written book is to give the reader who's interested in knowing more about turquoise, a general idea of where it comes from, how it's been used, and where to get it.

Turquoise has been used throughout the ages; it's been written about in history and because of its sky blue color it has been looked upon as a holder of magical powers. The Indians of the Southwest Americas have held this blue stone as an integral part of their lives since the time of its first discovery.

Perhaps it was a lonely hunter who had been out on a long, weary search for food, for many days with no luck. He stops for a drink of cool water when his eyes fall upon a sparkling blue stone in the stream. Where did it come from, this stone the color of the sky? He puts it in his hunting pouch and continues on his quest. But he did not have to go far, for a short distance from where he had found the blue stone was a most beautiful sight, a huge buck, big enough to feed his family for a long time. Was it the stone that had brought him the buck? He thought about this on his journey home. The stone must hold special powers and he decided that he must always have it with him when he goes hunting; it would bring him good fortune again.

This is only one story that tells how the turquoise stone may have attained its special meaning and came to be used so beautifully in Indian jewelry.

Until recently, the general public had neither been exposed to nor appreciated Indian turquoise jewelry. A piece of jewelry could be bought for a price far below the value of the artist's time to create it. In the last few years, Indian turquoise jewelry has been recognized as a true craft of great beauty. Current fashion trends have made it an "in" thing and this has driven the value of turquoise from a semi-precious gem to a precious one. *The Wall Street Journal* has been quoted as stating that turquoise was the second best investment next to diamonds. However, the article on turquoise was in the *National Observer,* March 17, 1973. This new value has given turquoise a new name: BLUE GOLD.

Indian Symbols

THUNDER BIRD	SACRED BEARER OF HAPPINESS UNLIMITED
SWASTIKA	GOOD LUCK
ARROW	PROTECTION ALL WAYS
CROSSED ARROWS	FRIENDSHIP
ARROWHEAD	ALERTNESS
4 AGES	INFANCY, YOUTH, MIDDLE AND OLD AGE
CACTUS	SIGN OF THE DESERT
GILA MONSTER	SIGN OF THE DESERT
CACTUS FLOWER	COURTSHIP
HORSE	JOURNEY
SADDLE BAGS	JOURNEY
BIRD	CAREFREE - LIGHTHEARTED
SNAKE	DEFIANCE, WISDOM
THUNDERBIRD TRACK	BRIGHT PROSPECTS
DEER TRACK	PLENTY GAME
BEAR TRACK	GOOD OMEN
RATTLESNAKE JAW	STRENGTH
SUN RAYS	CONSTANCY
HEADDRESS	CEREMONIAL DANCE
BUTTERFLY	EVERLASTING LIFE
MAN	HUMAN LIFE
RAIN CLOUDS	GOOD PROSPECTS
LIGHTNING AND LIGHTNING ARROW	SWIFTNESS
SWASTIKA WITH CIRCLE	4 CORNERS OF THE WORLD—LAKE IN CENTER
DAYS AND NIGHTS	TIME
MORNING STARS	GUIDANCE
SUN SYMBOLS	HAPPINESS
RUNNING WATER	CONSTANT LIFE
RAINDROP-RAIN	PLENTIFUL CROPS
HOGAN	PERMANENT HOME
TEPEE	TEMPORARY HOME
SKY BAND	LEADING TO HAPPINESS
MEDICINE MAN'S EYE	WISE—WATCHFUL
WARDING OFF EVIL SPIRITS	
PEACE	
BIG MOUNTAIN	ABUNDANCE
LASSO	CAPTIVITY
FENCE	GUARDING GOOD LUCK
ENCLOSURE	FOR CEREMONIAL DANCES
EAGLE FEATHERS	CHIEF
TRAILS CROSSING	

INDIAN SYMBOLS — explaining the markings used by Indians on their handicraft

HISTORY

Photo Compliments of Senator Barry Goldwater

Turquoise has a long history. It has been discovered in excavations of Egyptian ruins dating back to their earliest civilization.

Many writings from the earliest of times mention "blue stones" being used for adornment. They are even mentioned in the Bible; but whether these could possibly be turquoise is still being investigated by many scholars.

The name turquoise was first used in the thirteenth century. It was during this century that Marco Polo found turquoise in use in Persia and China. It was believed that the stone had the magical power to protect the wearer from injury or dying in a fall. Pieces of stone were used by the Persians as amulets and were quite often attached to horses' bridles for this protection.

Knowledge of turquoise spread across Asia and finally to Europe with the opening of the trade routes. Turquoise was supposed to have been first brought to Europe by the way of Turkey, thus the name of "Turkish Stone" was given to it.

The mineral was found only in a few desert areas of Asia, the Sinai Peninsula and N.E. Egypt. Little did they know, at that time, that there was still another vast source yet to be discovered.

Long before Columbus and the Spanish conquest, turquoise was prized by the tribes of Mexico and the tribes of American Southwest Indians. It is known the Indians have made extensive use of turquoise since before the birth of Christ. The trading of turquoise was widespread, reaching from as far as the Yucatan of Mexico, north to Canada and from California to Mississippi and Arkansas in the East. This is known because of the thousands of turquoise objects that archaeologists have found in the excavations of various ruins throughout these areas. It has also been written in many chronicles of the Spanish explorers about their encounter with natives possessing turquoise and other gems and minerals. Throughout these old writings, the word chalchihuitl was referred to in describing green stones. There is still some dispute as to whether this word means turquoise (green colored pieces of turquoise) or jade. Both stones were used prominently among the Aztecs. Some authorities believe that chalchihuitl referred to all green stones. Others, however, believe that this was the Aztec word for jade. An interesting note is that the Navajo Indians still refer to turquoise by the word chalchihuitl.

It's still an interesting question. What is chalchihuitl? Is it green turquoise or jade? Or did the Spanish explorers make a mistake and simply call all green stones chalchihuitl?

Despite their confusion, the Spanish explorers heeded tales of vast riches to the north and their desire for wealth drove them on. They always found turquoise being used by the natives and they were told that it had come from the north. Their quest finally took them to the Arizona-New Mexico area and eventual colonization resulted. There has been much written in history books about the Spanish invasion and the Indians uprising to drive them from their land. Some historians believe that the Indians were forced to work the turquoise mines for the Spanish and this is what led to the Indian's uprising.

Besides the use of turquoise as money for trade it also was used for adornments. In most tribes it was a sign of wealth and importance. In some it was worn only by men while in others it was reserved only for the chief.

Turquoise was fashioned into necklaces, bracelets, armlets, rings and earrings. One of the most well-known discoveries of ancient turquoise beads, pendants, and carvings was made by archeologist George Pepper in 1896 at Pueblo Bonito in New Mexico. Thousands and thousands of pieces were uncovered in these burial sites. He believed that because of the enormous amount of turquoise it must have been a burial chamber of a priest and other important persons. One skeleton alone had 8,385 beads and more than 500 pendants, all of turquoise. An outstanding item that was found was a turquoise jewel basket. This cylindrical shaped basket, 6 inches high and 3 inches in diameter, was covered with a mosaic of 1,214 pieces of turquoise. The basket itself had deteriorated with time but the mosaic had been held together by pinon gum and the sand in which it had been buried. The basket contained over a thousand beads, 150 small pendants, and 22 large pendants. A great variety of carved birds, frogs and tadpoles were found, as well as many inlaid objects.

Pepper concluded that most of the turquoise had come from the Cerrillos district of New Mexico, a prehistoric excavation of great wealth.

The color blue has had a great importance among many cultures. The ancient Egyptians painted their god Amun this color and the Hindu god Vishnu is represented by blue. Blue symbolized heaven for the ancient Chinese as well as the Southwest Indians. To the Aztecs, blue was a sign of supreme authority.

There are many interesting beliefs as to the power of turquoise. In ancient times many believed that it could cure many diseases, even snake bites, epilepsy, and insanity.

Some stones (from certain mines) have a tendency to fade with time and exposure to light. This characteristic of fading gave rise to a lot of superstitious beliefs. For many centuries, it was believed that the color of the stone depended on the health of the owner of the stone.

Many of the Indian tribes believed that the gem had stolen its color from the sky. This gave it a mystical value and it became important to them in their religious beliefs and in their ceremonies.

Among the Pueblo Indians, the Zuni probably value turquoise more highly than do the others. Some necklaces that are used only during ceremonies have been handed down from father to the eldest son for generations.

Turquoise is often used in offerings to the gods. Zuni women offer ground corn and powdered turquoise as food for the gods.

The Navajos, as well as the Zuni, use fetishes made of turquoise, or of other stones with eyes of inlaid turquoise, to protect their flocks of sheep. A fetish is a unique item that's used among people of primitive cultures. It usually is a natural object that is thought by the people to have special powers of some sort. This natural object may be most anything, such as a feather, a piece from a sacred tree, turquoise beads, etc. It may be of a personal nature, in that an object that may hold some special power for one person may mean nothing to another. A fetish may, however, hold some power that is observed by the entire culture. Among the Southwest Indians, corn and cornmeal is very sacred because it's a staple part of their life, so is the lifegiving rain. An Apache medicine man could not function without his turquoise, for he believed that it could bring rain.

The Hopi symbol of good fortune is the turquoise. The women still wear mosaic ear pendants that are characteristic of their tribe. The Hopi also have a very elaborate system of religious ceremonies. Many of the Kachinas, or gods, have turquoise as part of their adornments. They have a turquoise Kachina, too. Many of their Kivas, places of worship, have pieces of turquoise in the beams and posts.

Pima braves often pierced their noses and hung pieces of turquoise from them as decoration.

No metal mountings were used by the Southwest Indians until recent times. Necklaces and bracelets were of beads with holes drilled in the center for stringing. Mosaics, used in ear pendants or for decorating objects, were made by glueing pieces of stone with pinon gum onto a background such as wood, a shell, etc. The use of silver for mountings did not come into practice until the 1880's.

Silversmithing had been practiced by the Navajos some time before they started setting stones into their work. Iron smithing was learned from the Mexican smiths who lived in villages in the upper part of the Rio Grande valley. This was around 1850. Sometime between 1850 and 1870 the Navajos learned to work with silver, which led to stone se'.ting. American silver coins were their chief source of metal until the United States Government stopped it. Mexican pesos were then used until the Fred Harvey Co. began the commercial selling of silver in 1899.

Except in the Southwest, turquoise is most often set in gold. The yellow color of the gold makes for quite a different background than that of the light color of silver. The light blue stones are used with gold because the paler color blends so richly with the yellow metal; often the blue is so pale that it would not have the same rich effect with silver.

Notes on Certain Aspects

of Turquoise

BY
Stuart A. Northrop
Research Professor of Geology, Emeritus
University of New Mexico,
Albuquerque, New Mexico

Name

It is curious that although most dictionaries give the spelling as *turquoise,* most mineralogists have long used the spelling *turquois.* The name was given, not because the mineral came from Turkey but because it was introduced into the European market from Persia by way of Turkey. One English writer in 1652 referred to it as "Turky stone." In old French it was spelled *tourques,* later changed to *turquoise.* In German it is *turkis,* and in Spanish, *turquesa.* Names in many other languages are given by Pogue (1915, p. 129).

The Chalchihuitl Question

Ancient Spanish writers made numerous references to a green ornamental stone highly prized by the Aztecs of Mexico and generally called *chalchihuitl.* I have found sixteen variant spellings of this word (Northrop, 1959, p. 532). There has been much speculation concerning the mineralogical identity of this material. In several papers W.P. Blake (1858, 1883) argued that the green turquoise of New Mexico should be called chalchihuitl. Apparently, in old Mexico much of this was jade; see Foshag's (1955) paper entitled *Chalchihuitl*

– *A study in jade,* which does not even mention turquoise. Foshag notes that all Meso-American jade is the mineral jadeite and that most of it may have come from Guatemala, not Mexico.

Changes in the World's Gem and Precious Stone Industry According to S.H. Ball (1935, p. 1193-1194),

"Through the ages the precious stone industry has seen notable changes both as to the principal gem mined and the country of its source. From about 25000 to 3400 B.C., the Baltic amber mines dominated the industry. For the next 1425 years the turquoise mines of the Sinai Peninsula were the most important gem mines in the world. From about 1925 to 800 B.C., the emerald mines of the Egyptian Red Sea coast were unrivalled. Thereafter, until 1725 A.D., India and Ceylon, with their diamond, ruby, and sapphire mines, were the world's leading gem producers. They lost this position to the Brazilian diamond mines, which in turn were supplanted in 1870 by the South African diamond mines."

These major changes in the industry are shown in the accompanying chart, scaled approximately from 3400 B.C. to A.D. 1975.

Turquoise in the Old World

Amber, which is fossil resin and not truly a mineral, was used as an ornamental material many thousands of years ago. Turquoise was apparently the first true mineral utilized extensively as a precious or semiprecious stone, and the Sinai workings are the oldest turquoise mines in the world. Ball's (1927) paper entitled *Pharoahs mined turquoise in 3200 B.C.* described the large and highly organized expeditions dispatched from Egypt to the Sinai Peninsula. The forces sometimes numbered 2,000 to 3,000 men and were accompanied by military escorts of several hundred soldiers. The tools used were of stone; copper wedges were not introduced until about the year 2000 B.C. The expeditions from Egypt continued until about 1100 B.C.

Hopi Kachina Doll and Turquoise adornments from Don Hoel Collection. From left to right: Top-grade Lone Mountain nuggets, unusual Persian Jocla, superior Bisbee blue and coral chunks, top-grade Fox Mine Blue necklace, top-grade Morenci nuggets. Prices from $1,000.00 to $5,000.00 per piece. (1974) Photo Courtesy of Manley Photo-Tucson, Ariz.

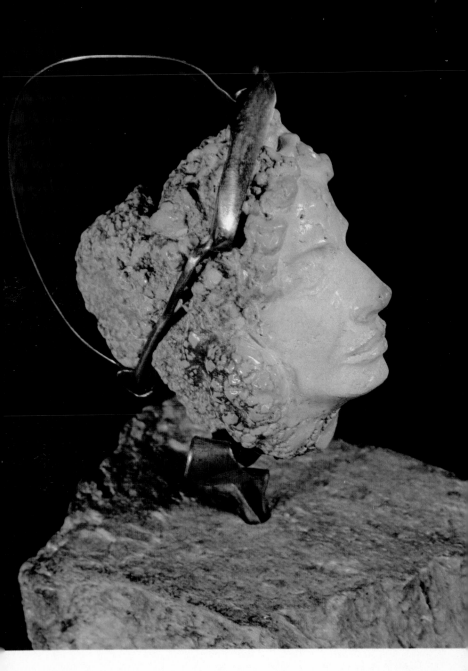

This fine turquoise head was done by Marvin Wilson, whose work has been featured before in Rock and Gem. He works in a variety of materials and is a recognized expert and teacher in carving. Photo by Jeff Kurtzeman.

An assortment of nuggets and finished jewelry. Photo courtesy of Manley Photo-Tucson, Ariz.

Top left: Navajo Persian sandcast. Top right: Persian sandcast Navajo. Bottom left: Blue gem Navajo overlay. Bottom right: Old pawn spiderweb. Photo Courtesy of Manley Photo-Tucson, Ariz.

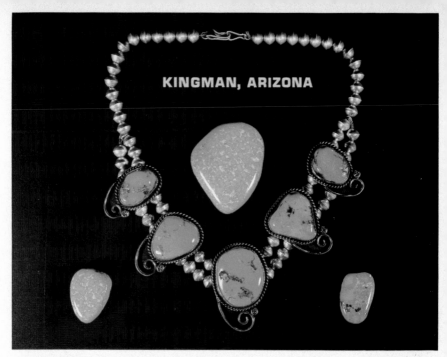

Finished jewelry and stones from the Kingman, Arizona Mine. Photo by Jeff Kurtzman.

This fine piece of Navajo work was done using turquoise from a locality far more famous for gold, Cripple Creek, Colorado. Photo by Jeff Kurtzman.

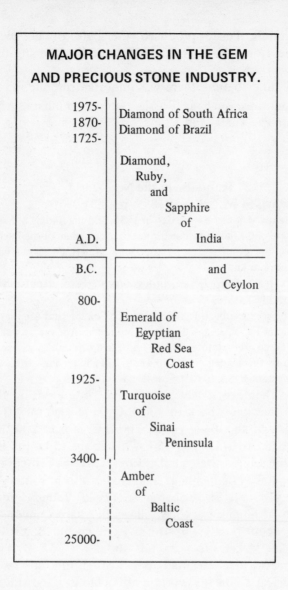

MAJOR CHANGES IN THE GEM AND PRECIOUS STONE INDUSTRY.

1975-	Diamond of South Africa
1870-	Diamond of Brazil
1725-	
	Diamond,
	Ruby,
	and
	Sapphire
	of
A.D.	India
B.C.	and
	Ceylon
800-	
	Emerald of
	Egyptian
	Red Sea
	Coast
1925-	
	Turquoise
	of
	Sinai
	Peninsula
3400-	
	Amber
	of
	Baltic
	Coast
25000-	

The most important deposits of the Old World are those at Nishapur in Persia (Iran) — birthplace of Omar Khayyam. Considerable doubt surrounds the date of earliest mining; some writers think it may have been as early as 2100 B.C.

But certainly Persia produced the bulk of the world's turquoise from about A.D. 1000 until the opening of the present century.

From time to time there was important production from other countires, such as Russia, Turkey, Bokhara, Afghanistan, Arabia, Tibet, and China.

Turquoise in the New World

According to W.P. Blake (1899, p. 283),

"Before my visit to New Mexico in 1858, and the finding at Santa Fe of green turquoise in use for necklaces by some of the Pueblo Indians, the occurrence of turquoise in America had not been announced or known."

In his textbook, *Economic geology,* Prof. Heinrich Ries (1937, p. 315) states that

"Turquoises have been found in the Los Cerillos [sic] Mountains near Santa Fe, N.M., and Turquoise Mountain, Arizona, as well as in Colorado. It is interesting to note that turquoise was hardly known in the United States in 1890, but some comes from the southwestern states."

But archeologists have discovered turquoise in South America that dates back to 900 B.C., in Mexico to 700 B.C., in Arizona to about the period 200 B.C. − A.D. 200, and in New Mexico to A.D. 734-757. What seems to be the oldest find in the United States is Dr. Emil W. Haury's discovery of two turquoise ornaments at Snaketown ruin in southeastern Arizona. Dr. F.H.H. Roberts, Jr. (1929) found turquoise pendants at Shabik' eshchee Village, in Chaco Canyon, New Mexico, about 7 miles upstream from Pueblo Bonito. This late Basket Maker site was built about 734-757. By far the most spectacular accumulation of turquoise in any archeological dig in the world is at Pueblo Bonito, which was occupied during the period 900-1130. The famous Hyde Expedition recovered more than 50,000 pieces of turquoise in 1897-99, and the total to date exceeds 65,000 pieces.

Pepper (1905) described and illustrated a number of inlaid items, such as a bone scraper inlaid with jet and turquoise, a jet frog with turquoise eyes, a buckle or breast ornament of jet inlaid with turquoise, and a number of beads, pendants, and carved birds — all of turquoise. A few years later Pepper (1909) described the spectacular contents of a small burial room about 6 feet square, which, among many other items, included the amazing total of 24,932 turquoise beads and more than 700 turquoise pendants. One skeleton had associated with it a total of 5,891 beads and small pendants. A still more gorgeously arrayed skeleton had 8,385 beads and more than 500 pendants, originally worn as wristlets, anklets, and ornaments on the breast and abdomen. On the left wrist alone were 2,388 beads and 194 small pendants. A small cylindrical basket nearby, 6 inches high and 3 inches in diameter, was covered by a mosaic of 1,214 small pieces of turquoise; within this basket were 2,150 beads, 152 small pendants, and 22 large pendants. Judd (1925) found a string of 2,500 turquoise beads which he described and illustrated in color.

Several workers are convinced that turquoise was an important item of trade in prehistoric times. According to Ball (1941, p. 17, 25),

"New Mexican turquoise reached Mexico City and the Mayan cities," and the early trade in Southwestern turquoise extended "from the West Indies and Yucatan on the south to Ontario on the north . . . and from California on the west to Mississippi and Arkansas on the east."

It should be noted that we do not yet know the source of most turquoise found in many Indian ruins. It was long assumed that most of the Chaco Canyon turquoise had come from the mines at Cerrillos. Pottery shards at the Cerrillos mines have been dated as 1150 to 1650 (Snow, 1973, p. 41). And Sigleo (1970, p. 75) stated that "there is no apparent evidence for extensive mining activity in the Cerrillos area prior to the Pueblo IV Period (approximately 1300 to 1700 A.D.)." Using spectrographic analysis of trace elements, Sigleo suggested that some of the Chaco Canyon turquoise came from certain mines in Arizona and Colorado.

(Incidentally, about 40 minerals — 21 species and 19 additional varieties — were utilized by the early inhabitants of Chaco Canyon during the period 750-1150. *See* Northrop, 1959, p. 7, for a list of these minerals.)

The accompanying chart, scaled from 3400 B.C. to A.D. 1975, shows dates of mining operations, dates of turquoise recovered in certain ruins, and dates of historical records.

There is abundant evidence of prehistoric mining of turquoise in five States — Colorado, New Mexico, Arizona, California, and Nevada. One writer reported recently that there are at least 38 such localities in Nevada alone. Some of the mines are simply surface workings in pits and trenches, but there are also underground operations such as shafts and tunnels. In fact, Jones (1909, p. 1) went so far as to declare "that no turquoise deposits of any note have ever been found in the west that did not show the evidence of prehistoric mining."

Thus many modern "discoveries" of turquoise in the Southwest were in all probability actually rediscoveries by prospectors of deposits that had been worked in prehistoric time. Dates of these modern "discoveries" in several States are as follows:

1858 — New Mexico
1870-75 — Nevada
1878 — Colorado
1883 — Arizona
1884 — Texas
1897 — California

For more detailed accounts, *see* Northrop (1973) and Snow (1973).

Historical Records, 1535-1700

Early accounts of Spanish exploring expeditions in northern Mexico, Arizona, and especially New Mexico reveal that the Indians had an abundance of turquoise beads, pendants, and various inlaid ornaments. A few of these references in chronological order are given here.

1535 — Alvar Nunez Cabeza de Vaca and three companions may have been in New Mexico. Later, while in Mexico, they saw turquoise, which the Indians told them came from the north.

HISTORICAL AND ARCHEOLOGICAL DATES FOR TURQUOISE.

	1975-	
	1858-	Rediscovery by Blake
	1700-	
		Mention by Spanish explorers
	1540-	
		Mining at Cerrillos dated by pottery
	1130-	
		Pueblo Bonito, N.M.
	900-	
	750-	Shabik' eshchee, N.M.
A.D.	200-	Snaketown,
B.C.	200-	Arizona
		Mexico
		South America
	900-	
	1100-	
		Egyptian
		mining
		in
		Sinai
		Peninsula
	3400-	

1539 — Fray Marcos de Niza, Esteban (or Estevan, a Negro or Arab from Morocco), and others started out from Mexico, heading for Cibola (Zuni, New Mexico). They had heard that there was an abundance of turquoise at Cibola; in his report Fray Marcos mentioned turquoise fourteen times. Esteban, who had been sent ahead to explore, "arrived there laden with a large number of turquoises and with some pretty women, which the natives had given him." Another writer noted that Esteban was loaded with turquoises "on his arrival at the outposts of Cibola, where he was killed and his turquoises confiscated."

1540 — Captain-General Francisco Vazquez de Coronado and a large expedition reached Cibola on July 7. Here they found turquoise and other minerals. In his narrative of the expedition, Castaneda mentioned an abundance of turquoise near Pecos, New Mexico, presumably from Cerrillos.

1629 — Fray Geronimo de Zarate Salmeron worked in New Mexico from 1621 until 1626. In his *Relaciones,* published in 1629, he mentioned "mines of turquoise," and wrote: "Before all things, there are mineral deposits, and there is no corner which has them not."

1630 — Fray Alonzo de Benavides, in his *Memorial,* mentioned turquoise mines being worked by Indians.

1697 — Fray Agustin de Vetancurt, in his *Cronica,* specifically mentioned turquoise mines at Cerrillos.

Sources of these historical records are given by Northrop (1959, p. 9-17, 530-531).

References Cited

Ball, S.H., 1927, Pharoahs mined turquoise in 3200 B.C.: Eng. and Min. Jour., v. 123, no. 12, March 19, p. 483-485.

Ball, 1935, Precious and semiprecious stones (gem minerals), *in* Minerals Yearbook 1934: U.S. Bur. Mines, p. 1193-1212.

Ball, 1941, The mining of gems and ornamental stones by American Indians: Smithson. Inst. Bur. Am. Ethnology Bull. 128, Anthropol. Papers 13, 77 p.

Blake, W.P., 1858, The chalchihuitl of the ancient Mexicans: Its locality and association, and its identity with turquoise: Am. Jour. Sci. (2), v. 25, p. 227-232.

Blake, 1883, New locality of the green turquois known as chalchuite, and on the identity of turquois with the callais or callaina of Pliny:

Am. Jour. Sci. (3), v. 25, p. 197-200.

Blake, 1899, Aboriginal turquoise mining in Arizona and New Mexico . . .: Am. Antiquarian and Oriental Jour., v. 21, p. 278-284.

Foshag, W.F., 1955, Chalchihuitl — A study in jade: Am. Mineralogist, v. 40, p. 1062-1070.

Jones, F.A., 1909, Notes on turquoise in the Southwest; Concerning its original workings, its geology and its modern method of mining: south-Western Mines, v. 1, no. 12, Sept. 5, p. 1-2.

Judd, N.M., 1925, Everyday life in Pueblo Bonito: Nat. Geographic Mag., v. 48, p. 227-262.

Northrop, S.A., 1959, Minerals of New Mexico: Albuquerque, Univ. New Mexico Press, 665 p.

Northrop, 1973, Turquoise: El Palacio, v. 79, no. 1, p. 3-22.

Pepper, G.H., 1905, Ceremonial objects and ornaments from Pueblo Bonito, New Mexico: Am. Anthropologist, n.s., v. 7, p. 183-197.

Pepper, 1909, The exploration of a burial-room in Pueblo Bonito, New Mexico, *in* Anthropological essays: Putnam Anniv. vol.: New York, G.E. Stechert & Co., p. 196-252.

Pogue, J.E., 1915, The turquois: A study of its history, mineralogy, geology, ethnology, archaeology, mythology, folklore, and technology: Nat. Acad. Sci. Mem., v. 12, pt. 2, mem. 3, 162 p.

Ries, Heinrich, 1937, Economic geology, 7th ed.: New York, John Wiley & Sons, 720 p.

Roberts, F.H.H., Jr., 1929, Shabik' eshchee Village: A late Basket Maker site in the Chaco Canyon, New Mexico: Smithson. Inst. Bur. Am. Ethnology Bull. 92, 164 p.

Sigleo, A.M.C., 1970, Trace-element geochemistry of Southwestern turquoise: Univ. New Mexico unpub. master's thesis, 92 p.

Snow, D.H., 1973, Prehistoric Southwestern turquoise industry: El Palacio, v. 79, no. 1, p. 33-51.

Postscript

In his book, *Minerals of New Mexico,* Northrop gives an extended account of turquoise in that State, including spelling and derivation of name, bibliography, records of occurrence, value of production, prehistoric mining, archeology, mention by early Spanish explorers, the chalchihuitl question, mythology and folklore, and technology (p. 520-535). In addition he (p. 5-9) describes the prehistoric utilization of many other minerals, and (p. 9-49) notes early records of occurrence and mining operations from 1535 on.

Lone Mountain Turquoise Sea Foam $1600.00. Treasure Trails Inc. Disneyland Plaza.

TURQUOISE

Photo Compliments of Senator Barry Goldwater

Turquoise Ore

Turquoise is hydrous aluminum phosphate colored by copper salts. It's deposited by water action and materials occur as nuggets, in veins, or crusts. The mother rock in which the turquoise is found, often called the matrix, is responsible for the markings or designs that appear in the turquoise. This matrix can be thin black lines, black or brown patches, iron pyrites, or even bits of quartz.

The quality and value of turquoise depends upon its color, hardness, and matrix. The finest turquoise is found in Persia, but the largest quantity used for jewelry comes from the United States. Some of this material is very near that of good quality Persian turquoise.

Persian turquoise refers to a top grade stone that's of a pure medium blue color. The color is uniformly even without flaws. The stone is very compact so that a very fine polish can be obtained and is translucent on thin edges. Most of these high quality pure stones are sold in the Near East countries and India. A small portion reaches Europe and the United States.

Matrix often creates very attractive patterns and contrasts, although it will never, never bring the price of a pure colored piece.

Spider web or cobweb turquoise refers to a high quality stone with a network of fine black lines which divides the surface into design of even patches. Its appearance makes its name obvious.

Matrix turquoise is a lesser grade of stone with thicker lines in a more irregular, uneven patch-like design.

Mottled Matrix is turquoise with two shades of blue or green showing, and it may or may not contain foreign material.

The value of turquoise begins to drop as green tinges appear; however, green turquoise is preferred by many Mexican artists. Some of the green turquoise is very pleasing to the eye, so it should be remembered that both color and markings are a matter of personal taste.

Value also decreases as the material becomes porous because these stones will not take a good polish and have no translucency. Very porous stones can be detected by a tongue test. By touching your tongue to the gem stone there is a definite "sticking" action due to the high absorption of the saliva which causes the tongue to dry out. If you get a smooth cut stone, the test will really work. However, another note should be interjected here, this test does not work with stones that have been treated with other materials. Porous types of stones are commonly treated with waxes, oils, or plastics to fill the pores and is a way of improving the color artificially. Such stones are likely to revert to their original shade with time and wear.

Now, the question — How can I tell a real stone from a fake one? It takes some practice in observation. We would suggest going to a reputable dealer who knows his stones and ask to see various qualities. Then, look at them and feel them and get acquainted with the different materials.

Artificial coloring is not a new idea, but has been known and practiced for a long time. It's been stated that in the thirteenth century the color of turquoise was heightened by using mutton fat or butter. The Southwest Pueblo Indians used tallow or grease in which to soak their turquoise. And the natives of Persia would carry the stones in their mouths before a sale to improve the color by moisture. A modern variation of this is to freeze stones for a period of time. The richer color will remain for a time but will gradually fade to its original shade.

Sometimes stones that are off-colored are stained with Prussian Blue dye. Stained stones will appear blue-grey and dull in artificial light. There are ways of testing stones to determine if they have been stained. Dye can be dissolved by washing with alcohol, wiping, and soaking in ammonia. However, if the stone is a true one, the process could be harmful; so it's advisable that the testing be done on the back side of the stone, thus preventing any damage to the face surface. A less drastic test is to scrape the back surface with the blade of a steel knife. Also on today's market, there is a patented process by which a permanent coloration can be given turquoise.

Along with color improvements there are many imitations available. This is not a new idea either for turquoise has been imitated as early as the ancient Egyptians. Much of today's inexpensive jewelry make use of these cheaper imitations.

First, many stones resemble turquoise naturally, or can be made to do so by using dyes or stains. To sell such stones as turquoise would be a fraud. Quite often they are confused with turquoise, such as some types of chalcedony, known as blue chrysoprase or artifically stained chalcedony. Sometimes, but rarely, lapis lazuli is mistaken for turquoise. This stone has a deeper blue, darker than a delphinium, with flecks of gold colored grains of pyrite. For those who like the green turquoise, malachite, chrysocolla, variscite, or green chalcedony might be mistaken for it. As a rule, when stones are cut and polished it is easier to distinguish true from look alikes; whereas, in their rough, natural state more mistakes in identity might be made.

Second, blue glass or enamel is the most common imitation used. It has a very glassy appearance and lacks real beauty. It's usually very easy to pick out and is used in a great deal of cheap jewelry.

Synthetic turquoise is the third type of imitation. These, through modern technology, are man-made to a high quality. Close examination or ordinary tests won't reveal their true identity. If you have an extra piece to experiment with, here is a good test: heat a small piece in a small, covered container. An artificial stone will melt to a dark-colored slag; whereas, a true piece of turquoise will crackle and turn into dark-colored powder.

Prize Pyote Bird Necklace set $1200. Hozuna Traders, Garden Grove, California.

Navajo high grade perfectly matched Morenci turquoise, complete set $4200. Treasure Trails, Inc., Disneyland Plaza.

MINING

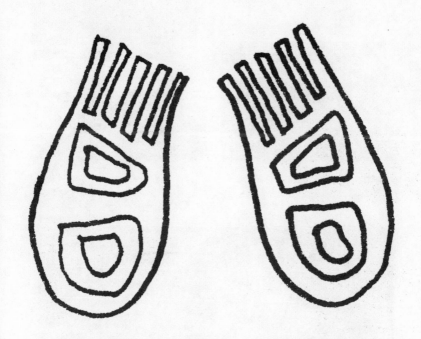

California Gem Mine near Barstow, an old Indian mine now being reopened.

Turquoise is found in arid, hot, and often waterless locations. It is mined on a small scale in the United States, mainly in Colorado, New Mexico, Arizona, Nevada and some desert portions of California. Since these areas are in an undesirable climate, work is done on a part-time basis during the best time of the year.

Practically every mine that has given a moderate quantity of turquoise was mined by American Indians before the arrival of the Spanish. One of the oldest and largest early mines is located near Cerrillos, New Mexico. It goes two hundred feet under the ground and is three hundred feet wide at some point; the whole north side of a solid rock mountain in this area. It is thought that this was probably the chief source of turquoise for the ancient Aztecs, who used so much in their works of art. That means that thousands of tons of rocks were broken out without the aid of modern machinery. It seems incredible that such an enormous excavation could have been accomplished. Ancient tools have been found in many old mines that give us an idea of how early mining was done. Hammers and mauls made of stone were used for breaking up the rocks, and picks made of antler have been found. Leather buckets, woven baskets, and coiled clay were used for carrying the ore out of the mines. Many of these implements had been decorated with bits of turquoise.

Another method used for extracting the stone was to build a fire next to the rock wall to heat it and then to throw cold water against it, causing the precious blue stone to crack away.

Some of the earlier turquoise was found in saucer-like "surface mines". These ran fifteen to thirty feet wide and approximately five or ten feet deep.

In later days, mining became more up-dated with the coming of the gold rush. Deep shafts and tunnels could be dug and large underground workrooms made it possible to remove the desired stones from the rock. This meant less work as the heavy rocks didn't have to be carried long distances.

Photos show California Gem Mine and large nuggets taken from this mine.

Today it still takes a great deal of man hours to mine turquoise ore. Bulldozers are used for breaking up the ore and some types of mother rock can be separated from the stone by tumbling it in a cement mixer with water.

Little Gem Turquoise Mine Austin, Nevada.

Some of these old mines are still worked today; however, most of them have been worked out or lost over the years.

It is interesting to note that none of today's mines are owned by Indians.

Since turquoise is often a by-product of copper, much material has been lost to copper smelters; but quite often this job of extracting the turquoise is contracted out before mining the copper proceeds.

Mine Locations

Prehistoric workings of turquoise have been found in many districts of Arizona, Nevada, Colorado, California and New Mexico.

New Mexico has produced more turquoise than any other state. The four main regions are: the Cerrillos Hills, Burro Mountains, Little Hachita Mountains, and the Jarilla Hills of Otero County.

Little Gem Turquoise Mine Austin, Nevada. Ray Feaster and Rick Rangel.

Turquoise Hills and Mount Chalchihuitl, the latter being an extensive example of prehistoric mining, are located in the Cerrillos district of Santa Fe County. The Burrow Mountains of Grant County are located in the southwest corner of New Mexico. The Azure mine was opened in 1891 and it produced between $2,000,000 and $4,000,000. Some of the finest Persian quality gems come from the Azure. The biggest single deposit ever recorded was the famous "Elizabeth pocket." Turquoise Mountain is the prominent elevation in the Little Hachita Mountains of Grant County. Turquoise Mountain is justly named because it is the site of many productive mines.

In Arizona the most extensive aboriginal mining site is in Mineral Park of Mojave County. Ithaca Peak and Aztec Mountain are the principle locations within the Cerbat range.

San Bernardino County in California has prehistoric mining sites in the Turquoise Mountains. Also, some principal deposits are in the Mojave Desert.

Prehistoric mining was carried on in Conejos and Lake Counties in Colorado.

Nevada's workings are found in Clark and Nye counties, where prehistoric mining was carried on. Esmeralda County is another source of turquoise. Although New Mexico is the all-time leader in turquoise production, Austin of Lander County, Nevada, is currently the leading gem quality producer of turquoise in the Western United States. This finding was recently published in the Austin newspaper.

Following are some general locations of well-known mines and mountain areas where good to fine quality turquoise has been mined. Most often turquoise pieces are named after the mines from which they come. For instance, Bisbee turquoise or Lone Mountain turquoise came from the mines of the same names. An expert in turquoise can tell, by looking at a piece, from what area and/or mine it originated.

If you are interested in more and/or specific locations, information may be obtained from any State agency.

Azure Mine. Grant County, New Mexico. Located in Burro Mountain. Fine quality stones of bright blue color.

Battle Mountain Area. Lander County, Nevada. There are various mines in this area. Stones from this area are referred to as "Battle Mountains." Stones bright blue with brown matrix.

Little Gem Turquoise Mine Austin, Nevada using jack hammer to cut out vein of turquoise.

Bisbee Mine. Cochise County, Ariz. Near Bisbee. Stones of good color with dark matrix.

Blue Boy Mine. Esmeralda County, Nevada. Stones dark blue. Some dark brown and black matrix.

Blue Gem Mine, Lander County, Nevada. Near Battle Mountain. Stones clear blue and also some fine green color.

Burro Mountain Area. Grant County, N. Mexico. Located in southwest corner of the state.

California Gem Mine, San Bernardino County, Calif.

Cameo Mine. Grant County, N. Mex. Part of Robinson and Porterfield mines located on Turquoise Mountain in Little Hachita Hills. Stones pure blue.

Castillian Mine. Santa Fe County, N. Mex. In Cerrillos area. Stones fine Persian blue quality.

Cerrillos Area. Santa Fe County, N. Mex. Location of Mt. Chalchihuitl, site of prehistoric mining.

Cripple Creek. Teller County, Colo. near Colorado Springs. Stone light to dark with brown matrix.

Fox Mine. Lander County, Nevada. Near Austin. Dark Blue with matrix some greenish blue.

Hymalaya Mine. San Bernardino County, Calif. Near Arizona-Nevada borders. Stones of light blue to dark. Prehistoric mining.

King Mine. Conejos County, Colo. Near Manassa. Stones from pale blue to bright blue. Some brown matrix and spider web.

Kingman Mine. Mohave County, Arizona. Near Kingman, Arizona. Stones clear blue. Some matrix.

Leadville area, Lake County, Colo. Near Leadville in central part of state. Many mines in this area. Turquoise from the area is referred to as "Leadville."

Lone Mountain Mine. Esmeralda County, Nevada. Near Tonopah. Stones clear blue and some spider web.

Little Gem Mine. Lander County, Nev. Near Austin. Owned by Ray and Kay Feaster.

Mineral Park Area. Mohave County, Arizona. Northwest corner around Kingman in the Cerbot Mountains. Mining at Aztec Peak and Ithaca Peak.

Morenci Mine. Greenlee County, Ariz. Near Morenci. Stones of bright blue with dark matrix.

Raw turquoise can be bought over the counter in some shops, photos from Hozuna Traders.

No. 8 Spider Web Mine. Eureka County, Nevada, near Tenabo, above Battle Mountain. Stones of finest quality spider web matrix.

Royal Blue Mine, Nye County, Nevada near Tonopah. Stones from pale to dark blue.

Sleeping Beauty Mine. Gila County. Near Globe. Stones pale blue.

Tiffany Mine. Grant County, N. Mex. Located at Cerrillos area near Cameo mine. Stones fine quality Persian blue.

Villa Grove, Saguchi County, Colo. Near Salida & Villa Grove. Stones bright blue.

Little Gem Mine Austin, Nevada. Ray Feaster and workman mining turquoise.

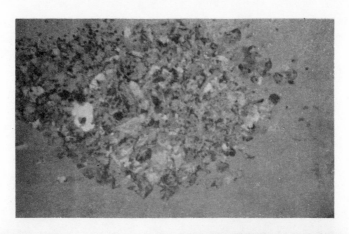

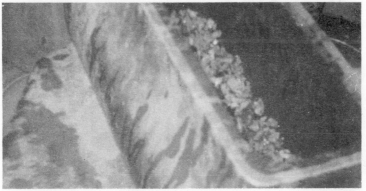

Large and small turquoise nuggets from Mc Ginness Mine.

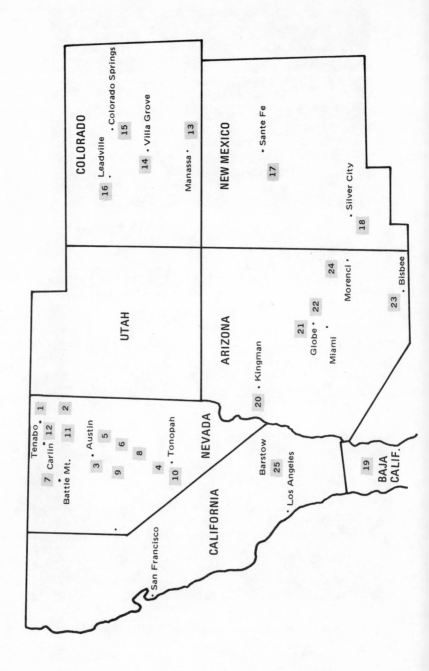

COLORADO

16 • Leadville
• Colorado Springs 15
14 • Villa Grove
Manassa • 13

NEW MEXICO

• Sante Fe 17

• Silver City 18

UTAH

ARIZONA

24 Morenci •
22 • Bisbee 23
Globe • 21
Miami •
20 • Kingman

Tenabo • 1
Carlin • 12 2
11 • Austin
Battle Mt. • 5
7 • 3 • 6 8
9 4
• Tonopah 10

NEVADA

CALIFORNIA

Barstow • 25
• Los Angeles

San Francisco •

BAJA CALIF. 19

Turquoise Treasures

1. Stormy Mountain Turquoise
   Mined Near Tenabo, Nevada
2. Steinich Turquoise
   Mined near Gold Acres, Nevada
   not active since 1967
3. Careyco Lake Turquoise
   Mined near Austin, Nevada
   active occasionally
4. Royston Royal Blue Turquoise
   Mined near Tonopah, Nevada
   active occasionally
5. McGinness Turquoise
   Mined near Austin, Nevada
   active occasionally
6. Red Mountain Turquoise
   Mined near Austin, Nevada
   not active since 1965
7. Blue Gem Copper Basin Turquoise
   Mined near Battle Mtn., Nevada
   active occasionally
8. Godbers Dry Creek or Burnham Turquoise
   Mined near Austin, Nevada
   active occasionally
9. Blue Diamond Turquoise
   Mined near Austin, Nevada
   active occasionally
10. Lone Mountain Turquoise
    Mined near Tonopah, Nevada
    active occasionally
11. Fox or Cortez Turquoise
    Mined near Tenabo, Nevada
    active occasionally
12. #8 Spiderweb Turquoise
    Mined near Carlin, Nevada
    not active since 1957
13. King's Blue Green Turquoise
    Mined near Manassa, Colorado
    not active since 1948

14. Villa Grove Turquoise
    Mined near Villa Grove, Colorado
    not active since 1965
15. Cripple Creek Turquoise
    Mined near Colorado Springs, Colorado
    not active since 1948
16. Leadville Turquoise
    Mined near Leadville, Colorado
    not active since 1962
17. Los Cerillos, Tiffany Turquoise
    Mined near Santa Fe, New Mexico
    not active since 1947
18. Santa Rita Turquoise
    Located near Silver City, New Mexico
    found in copper mine
19. Evans, Old Mexico Turquoise
    Mined in Baja California, Mexico
    not active since 1942
20. Kingman Turquoise
    Located near Kingman, Arizona
    found occasionally in copper mines
21. Sleeping Beauty Turquoise
    Located near Globe, Arizona
    found occasionally in copper mines.
22. Pinto Valley, or Castle Dome Turquoise
    Located near Miami, Arizona
    found occasionally in copper mines
23. Bisbee Turquoise
    Located in Bisbee, Arizona
    found occasionally in copper mines
24. Morenci Turquoise
    Located in Morenci, Arizona
    found occasionally in copper mines
25. California Gem Mine
    located in Barstow California
    wide variety of many types of turquoise

Miners manually digging turquoise.

Caterpillar surface excavating at Mc Ginness Mine in Austin, Nevada.

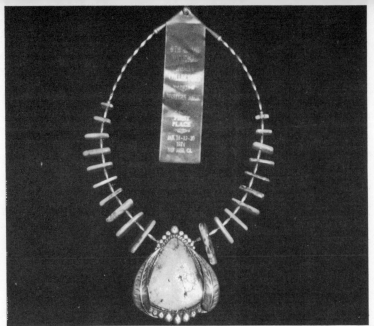

Prize 14 carats of Morenci turquoise $3500.00. Hozuna Traders, Garden Grove, California.

Santa Domingo shell necklace. Inlay with turquoise, brass and silver, note detail of brass drums. On the strand of green Nevada turquoise the companion of singular Coral National Kingman turquoise, and again Toni Aguliar's typical specimen of brass and turquoise. From the private collection of Mr. De Castro. Shell necklace ceremonial piece of Santo Domingo Indians at ceremonial. Single, big shell $550.00. Indian Trader Turquoise Teepee, Newport Beach, California.

LAPIDARY

Photo Compliments of Senator Barry Goldwater

MORENCI, ARIZONA

Finished and set pieces from Morenci, Arizona. Photo by Jeff Kurtzman.

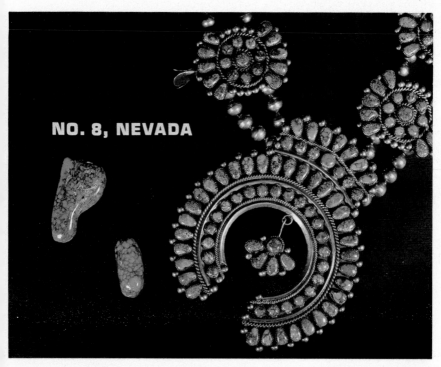

NO. 8, NEVADA

Excellent Zuni design work and turquoise from #8 mine Nevada, combine to form an attractive squash blossom necklace. Photo by Jeff Kurtzman.

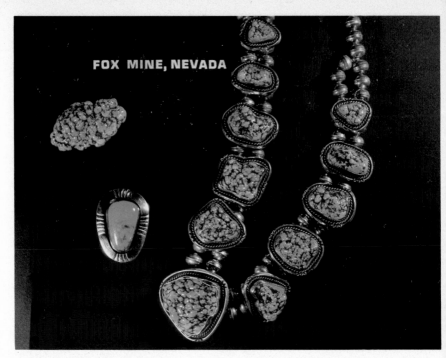

FOX MINE, NEVADA

Fox Mine, Nevada turquoise has been given several names; not the least of which is "Popcorn" turquoise. There's no doubt as to why such a name was applied to these lumpy nodules. Photo by Jeff Kurtzman.

A beginner could stumble across nodules of choice turquoise like this and miss them completely for they are enclosed in a "shell" of ugly limonite matrix. Once cut through, the nodule reveals fine spiderwebbing of the limonite in blue turquoise. These are from near Mina, Nevada. The larger piece is 3½" X 2" Photo by Jeff Kurtzman.

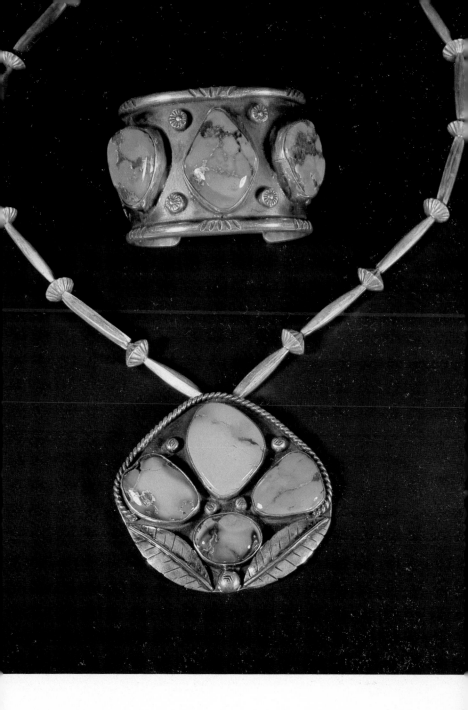

A brooch and necklace illustrating fine silversmithing in conjunction with turquoise.
Photo by Jeff Kurtzman.

Twenty-two matched pieces of fine turquoise woven into a captivating necklace. Photo by Jeff Kurtzman.

Since this is not a handbook on lapidary or silversmithing, but rather an informative introduction to turquoise and its possible uses in today's market, we will only touch the surfaces of these two very fascinating fields. It's important to include these two chapters because it is by this means that most of today's turquoise is utilized.

Jewelry making is the hobby of many people, and it is both fun and exciting to take a rough rock and turn it into something beautiful. If you are interested, there are many "how-to-do-it" craft books available at your library, book stores and rock shops. Many classes are given through adult education. Check with the local high schools for class schedules. Also junior colleges have classes in silversmithing and lapidary. It would be wise to check out these sources as it's a good way to see if you would like jewelry making before investing money in tools and equipment.

There are many outfits on the market in a wide price range. Cabochon cutting outfits run from around $100 and up. The cost of grits, buffs, and polishes is nominal and most other tools, pans, etc., can be found around the house.

Equipment for silversmithing will run quite a bit more (see the chapter on silversmithing for more detail). However, tumblers are very nominal in cost about $15.00 to $75.00. This would be a good starter and can be used by the entire family.

Gemcutting ranges from a simple cabochon cut to a multi-faceted cut of a fine diamond. The whole process of gemcutting is a series of progressive steps of abrasions, ranging from roughing out to a finer cut and still finer, until there are no bumps or scratches left.

A cabochon is a cut of stone most frequently used by amateur gemcutters. It is versatile because of the great variety of size, shape, colors, and materials that can be used. This dome shaped stone is used extensively in jewelry in today's market.

top   side

Let's take a simplified look at the formation of a cabochon. Since this book is about turquoise, the special techniques that must be taken into consideration when cutting and polishing turquoise will be included.

All gemstones have a degree of hardness and they are measured by the Mohs (rhymes with hose) Scales. This is an arbitrary table of 10 degrees with diamond, the hardest known mineral, at the top or number 10.

Here is the Mohs scale:

      1 – Talc
      2 – Gypsum
      3 – Calcite
      4 – Fluorite
      5 – Apatite
      6 – Feldspar
      7 – Quartz
      8 – Topaz
      9 – Corundum (ruby, sapphire)
    10 – Diamond

Turquoise is number 6 on the Mohs scale, which is considered a soft stone. (Remember, however, there are varying degrees of hardness within various qualities of turquoise).

SAWING – First, a slab must be cut from the stone. This is done on a diamond saw which looks like a woodworking saw. One major difference, however, is that there's a reservoir underneath to hold a lubricant. When the saw is running, the lower edge of the blade goes through the lubricant, which acts as a coolant to eliminate heat build-up while cutting a stone. The most common lubricant used for slabbing saws is a 50-50 mixture of kerosene and No. 20 grade motor oil. It

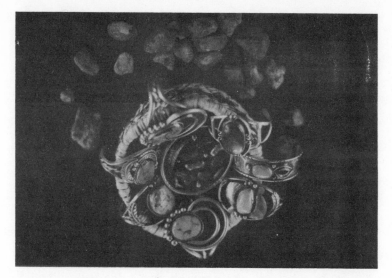

Navajo leaf bracelet $140.00 retail, 1 stone Navajo leaf bracelet $160.00 retail, Barefoot bracelet (Navajo) $160.00 retail, middle bracelet coral and turquoise $250.00 retail, leaf bracelet large stone $160.00 retail.

should be used with some caution as there is a fire danger. However, when cutting turquoise, water should be used as a coolant. Since turquoise is porous, it should be kept away from oil, as it will cause it to discolor and turn to an undesired shade of green.

The slab is cut 3/16" to 3/8" thick depending on its use, (i.e. thin for rings, thicker for pendants).

BLANKS – Next, comes the marking of the desired shape of the cabochon called a blank. This is done with an aluminum pencil and a template containing various sizes and shapes (round, oval, rectangle, small or large). The shape is then traced directly onto the slab. The excess stone is removed with a trim saw. Notches are then made around the edges, but not too close to the outline of the cabochon. The notches are then either "snipped" off with pliers or cut off with the trim saw.

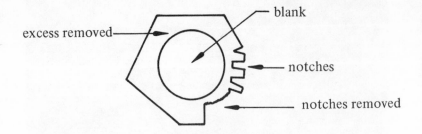

excess removed

blank

notches

notches removed

A trim saw has a thinner and smaller blade than the slabbing saw. Lubricant should be used the same as with the slabber.

DOPPING – Now, the stone is ready for dopping. Dopping is placing the stone on the end of a stick so that it will be easier to handle while grinding and sanding into the desired shape. A 6" piece of doweling is used and the stone is held in place with a piece of heated wax.

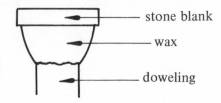

stone blank

wax

doweling

GRINDING – With the stone blank dopped, it is now ready to grind down into shape. The initial grinding is done on a powered wheel of bonded carborundum. It's a gritty substance much resembling sandpaper. First, a coarse wheel of 100 grit is used and the finer grinding is done on a 220 grit wheel. (Notice that the higher the number the finer the grit). The initial grinding on a piece of turquoise should be on a 220 grit because of its softness. The grinding is done by holding the dopped stone at about a 25° angle at a point below the middle of the wheel. A firm, even pressure is applied in a rotating motion, moving around and around and tilting it more and more until it's dome shaped. Turquoise must be kept wet during all stages of grinding and sanding. At no time should it be allowed to get hot or it will start to show white spots or even crack.

A beveled edge is cut around the bottom. This is a narrow, flat edge and is used when setting the stone in jewelry mounts.

Grinding grit wheel, stone being ground into shape.

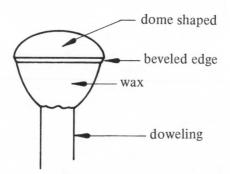

- dome shaped
- beveled edge
- wax
- doweling

SANDING — Once grinding is completed, the shape is defined to a greater degree by sanding. Scratches and bumps are sanded out on a powered wheel with wet sanding cloth of carborundum grit. The initial sanding uses a 120 grit and then a finer 220 grit. Turquoise requires an initial sanding with 220 grit followed by 400 grit and then a 600 grit, remembering always to keep the stone wet. After sanding is completed the stone is washed thoroughly to remove all of the grit.

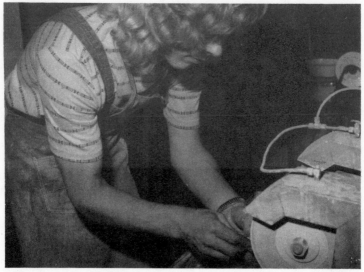

Polishing cabochon, Dave Quinn.

POLISHING — With all of the scratches and bumps removed the cabochon is ready for polishing.

Polishing is done with buffs made of felt or leather. These should be kept wet, also. Polishing agents of cerium oxide or tin oxide are used on most stones used for cabochons. Cerium oxide is used by most gemcutters but tin oxide gives turquoise a better polish.

Water is added to the tin oxide to make a creamy paste and is applied to the running buff with a paint brush. The dopped stone is then applied to the buff with very little pressure in a rotating, sweeping motion. Turquoise must be polished very carefully so as not to build up heat. A good quality stone will attain a beautiful high polish. A lesser grade or darker colored stone will tend to have a more velvety luster.

The stone is then removed from the dop by carefully holding it over an alcohol lamp to soften the wax. The stone can then be pulled off with the fingers. Extra wax can be removed by rubbing with a damp cloth.

Little Gem raw turquoise and polished stones mined in Austin, Nevada.

With turquoise, avoid the use of ammonia, soap or detergent as they will cause the color of the stone to turn. Now, the stone is ready for setting.

A fun and inexpensive way of starting lapidary is with tumblers. A tumbling machine resembles a small cement mixer. Tumbling takes a matter of days in progressive steps using various grits and polish and water.

Two things to remember are the selection of stones and the tumbling load. Different kinds of stones can be tumbled together but they must be of the same relative hardness. The tumbling load is important for the best results. If the tumbler is underfilled the stones will not polish. If it is overfilled, the movement of the tumbling action is choked. The proper load is one-half to three-quarters full.

The end result is a polished stone of a natural shape with

rounded, smooth surface. This kind of stone is very versatile in use, such as earrings, pendants, etc.

Such turquoise pieces can be obtained with the use of a tumbling machine. However, when tumbling turquoise, greater care must be taken because of its softer nature. Stones of similar hardness should be used and turquoise takes a shorter period of time to round off the edges.

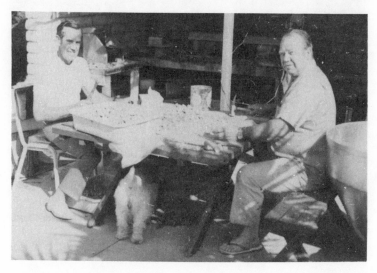

Cobbing rock mined from Little Gem Turquoise mine Austin, Nevada. In background lapidary equipment for cutting, polishing and tumbling turquoise. Chat Hatfield and Ray Feaster.

A popular Indian necklace is disk beads made of turquoise and shells. The most famous are from the Santo Domingan Indians, who have been making them for centuries. Their procedure is very interesting. They take some turquoise and grind off each side to make it flat, then it is broken into small bits. A hole is drilled into the center with a reciprocating drill (a rather primitive, hand-operated drill still in use today). The pieces are strung and then rolled over and over on sandstone until they are perfectly round. The better the grade of turquoise and the smaller the beads the greater the value.

Sometimes beads are strung with silver, jet and/or coral to make very interesting combinations.

Carving is another area of lapidary. Since it's a whole field of its own, it will not be dwelled up on in detail; but it should be mentioned because the Southwest Indians, especially the Zunis, have made stone carvings for hundreds of years. Turquoise, shell, coral, agate, and other colored stones have been carved into small birds and animals, then strung into necklaces. These are often called fetish necklaces. The name is misleading because these necklaces have no such symbolism to the Indians.

———————————

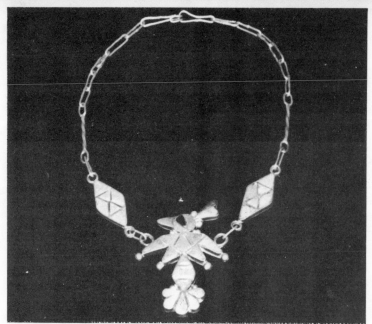

Cohen necklace. Zuni inlaid turquoise with handmade chain. An old piece where it can be noted that the color of turquoise has changed with age $650.00. Indian Trader Turquoise Teepee, Newport Beach, California.

From O.F. De Castro's private collection. Indian Trader Turquoise Teepee, Newport Beach, California.

SILVERSMITHING

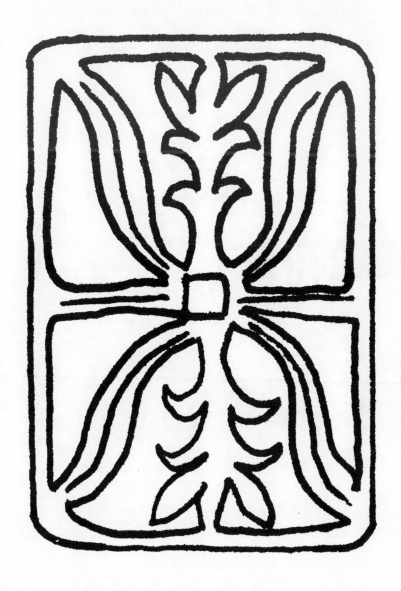

Photo Compliments of Senator Barry Goldwater

Silversmithing is a highly skilled art as is gemcutting. It is a hobby that's enjoyed by many and is another facet of jewelry making.

One of top Indian silversmiths Jane Popovich.

It should be remembered that this chapter is a very generalized look at silversmithing. It is an attempt to give you an idea of how the handmade jewelry that is found on today's market was made.

It is not a cheap hobby but an amateur can start with a minimum of equipment:

TORCH — An important piece is the blowtorch. Several kinds are available but the type that is most commonly used is the propane gas torch. The cheapest of this type uses a replaceable gas can, compared to the more expensive refillable gas cylinders. The latter cost more initially but are cheaper in the long run.

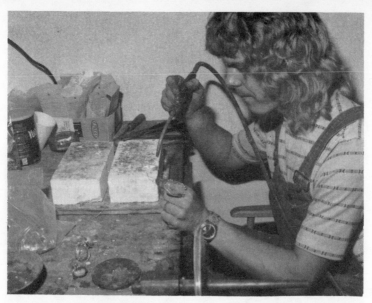

Custom silversmith Dave Quinn using torch in silversmithing.

Various tips are used on the torch for directing the heat. A wider angle would be used for overall heating such as in annealing; whereas a small pencil point flame would be used for pinpoint soldering. (approx. cost — replaceable cans $12.00, refillable cans $60.00).

TOOLS — Tools used in silversmithing are specialized and can be purchased at jewelry-supply houses. Here's a minimum tool list needed to begin:

1. Pliers — 1 flat-nosed, 1 round-nosed. (approx. cost — $3.00 ea.)
2. Steel tweezers — (approx. cost — $1.00)
3. Ball peen hammer — (approx. cost — $3.00)
4. Heavy files — 1 6" flat with med. cut, 1 6" round with med. cut. (approx. cost — $1.75 ea.)
5. Needle files — 1 knife edge, 1 half-round, (approx. cost — $.75 ea.)
6. Jeweler's saw, with 3/0 blades. (approx. cost — $5.00)
7. Combination bench pin (with vee cut) and anvil. (approx. cost — $6.50)
8. Copper tongs (for dipping pieces in pickle). (approx. cost — $2.50)

9. Emery paper and cloth — fine and med. grit. (approx. cost — $.25 ea.)
10. Asbestos pad (approx. cost — $1.75)

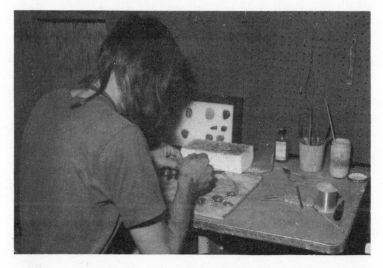

Steel tweezers used for handling small pieces of silver in silversmithing.

METALS — Gold, silver, and copper are the metals most used in jewelry making. Gold is the easiest to work with because of its lower melting point but it's also the most

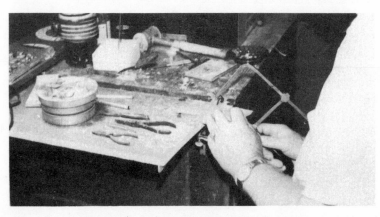

Cutting sheet of silver, silversmith Fritz Wright.

expensive. Copper has a very high melting point, 1083° Centigrade, and is difficult for an amateur. Silver has a melting point of 893° Centigrade for sterling silver.

Sterling silver is an alloy of fine silver and copper and it's the metal most used. Silver can be bought in sheet, wire, and grains (used for casting) and is priced by the Troy ounce. Many hobby centers sell silver plate by the square inch and wire by the foot. Both plate and wire come in various gauges or thicknesses. (Remember the higher the number, the thinner the thickness). Besides various gauges, wire comes in round, half-round, and square.

ANNEALING — First, the silver must be annealed before it can be worked into a desired shape. This is a process of heating the metal with a torch until it glows soft pink. Heating changes the internal structure and "softens" it so that it can be hammered or "pushed" into another shape. Annealing must be repeated throughout the work because hammering hardens the metal.

PICKLING — When metal is heated it becomes discolored or oxidized. To remove this darkened color, called fire scale, the metal is dipped in a pickle solution. Pickle is one part sulphuric acid to nine parts water. Only copper tongs should be used for dipping and the metal should be cooled before pickling.

SOLDERING — Soldering is a process by which two pieces of metal are joined together by bringing the solder to melting temperature. The solder then flows, fusing the two pieces together. It's important to make sure that the melting point of the solder is below that of the metal that is being worked on. Solder comes in easy, medium, and hard flows. These terms denote melting temperatures. Nothing is more exasperating than to have the metal start melting and the piece of solder just sitting there staring you in the face.

To prevent oxidization of the metal while soldering flux is used. This is a mixture of borax and water into a paste thickness which is brushed onto the surfaces. It can be bought in small bottles all ready to use.

Now, let's take a look at some of the techniques silversmiths use in jewelry-making.

HAMMERED WORK — One of the basic techniques of silverwork is hammered work or forging. A piece of silver, whether sheet or wire, is annealed and then hammered into the desired thickness, width, and shape. Afterwards, the surface is filed smooth and then it's ready for decoration, if desired.

Wire rope, droplets and scallops are quite often seen as decoration, especially in American Indian jewelry. Wire rope is made by bending a length of wire around a stationary object (i.e. a nail) and then taking hold of the two ends, twist the two wires together. Droplets are little balls of silver that are sometimes called raindrops. When small scraps of silver are heated to melting point, they will roll up into balls. These can then be soldered on. Scallops make a very decorative edge and are quite common in Indian Concha belts. Silver wire is wrapped around a round object (i.e. a nail or a knitting needle) to form a spiral. The two opposite sides are sawed in two, resulting in even shaped scallops. These pieces are then soldered in places.

Designs may also be cut into the surface with files.

A good piece of hand-hammered jewelry will have hammer marks on the back.

EMBOSSING — Embossing is a process of shaping a design into sheet metal from the back side. (From the front side the designs will be raised in appearance and touch). The piece of silver is annealed and then placed on a surface that has some "give" to it such as a pitch bowl or a wooden block. Small punches are then gently tapped with a hammer to drive simple forms into the metal. The ends of the punches have various shapes and used in combinations can make many intricate designs.

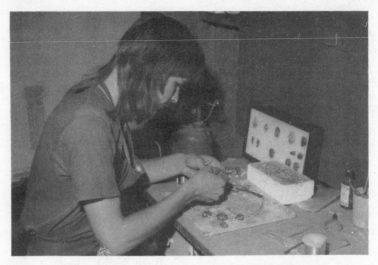

Embossing, process of shaping, Daniel S. Mayhew.

DAPPING — Dapping is similar to embossing in that the same procedure is used. The difference is that the shapes are simply round. A dapping block is made of soft steel with various sized round holes in it. Dapping dies (or punches) fit the holes accordingly. Sheet metal is then punched down into the depression forming a half dome shape. Beads can be formed this way by soldering two half domes together. Half domes are also used as buttons.

Dapping, Dave Quinn.

Stamping, Daniel S. Mayhew.

STAMPING – Stamping is the process of cutting a design into the metal, sort of the opposite of embossing. Steel punches, with designs cut into the ends, are tapped into the surface and the impression of the design is left. This process is used in many medias, such as leather tooling. Many punches or dies are made by the smiths with designs of their own creation.

Bezels.

BEZELS — Fine, transparent gems are often set in prong-type settings. Turquoise and other cabochon cut stones are most often set into jewelry by a bezel. This is a narrow strip of silver that holds the stone in place. The strip is fit securely and snuggly around the outside edge of the stone. Once it has been measured perfectly the ends are soldered together. The bezel is then soldered into place on the piece of jewelry. A cushion is sometimes placed in the bottom and then the stone is seated into the bezel. The bezel is rubbed with a smooth tool, such as a burnisher, to tighten it against the stone to hold it securely in place.

CHANNEL WORK — Some of the best channel work is done by the Zuni Indians. The base of the desired shape is made and then a narrow edged rim is soldered around the outside. The inside surface is then divided into channels to form the desired design. This is done by soldering strips of silver in place. Pieces of stone or shell are cut to fit into the provided spaces. The pieces are usually slightly recessed below the top edge of the silver strip. After all the stones are in place the silver strips are ground down flush to the stone level. This action forms a sort of a "bezel effect" to hold the stones in place. If this step is not used the stones are usually glued in. Channeling is a very tedious and painstaking job and

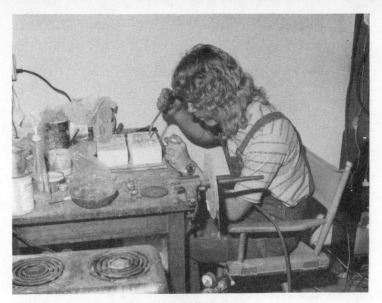

Chanel work, Dave Quinn.

it requires steady hands, a keen eye, and tons of patience. Jet, turquoise, coral, and shell are most commonly used by the Zunis.

Inlay, Jane Popovich.

INLAY — Inlaying is somewhat the opposite of channeling. Instead of the design being built up, it is cut into the piece of jewelry. The space is then filled with a piece of stone or shell cut to fit. It much resembles a mosaic of stones enclosed in a silver bezel.

Overlay, Daniel S. Mayhew.

OVERLAY — The base is made of sheet silver and cut into the desired shape. A second piece is cut to the same basic shape. The desired design is sawed out of this second piece. The result looks like a template with the designs being formed by the open, cut out spaces. The two pieces are then fitted together and "sweat soldered". Sweat soldering is a tricky job. Pieces of solder are placed on the surface of the initial piece of silver. The designed piece is then placed on top and then very carefully heated. The heat causes the solder to flow thus fusing the two pieces together. The resulting piece is one where the design then appears to be recessed. The recessed area is then treated with liver of sulfur which causes it to oxidize or turn black. The design then stands out in contrast to the total piece — a most pleasing effect. The Hopi Indians are noted for their beautiful overlay work.

Casting, Daniel S. Mayhew.

CASTING — Casting is a distinctive technique of silversmithing. Basically, a form of a design is cut into the block called a mold. Molten metal is poured into the mold, cooled, and then the cast piece is removed, cleaned, filed, and polished.

A mold can be made out of a variety of different materials such as charcoal or cuttlebone. The Navajo's use sandstone or a very hard clay for their fine, intricate designs. The material must be tough and fine grained, but soft enough for carving.

Two even-sized blocks are used, rubbed together to make the face surfaces smooth until they fit together perfectly. Then the design is cut into only one of the pieces. A sprue (or opening) is cut from the outside edge to the design. This is the channel in which the molten metal will flow through to fill in the space of the carving. Also several air vents are cut. The cut design is rubbed with a fatty substance or something similar to prevent the metal from sticking. The two blocks are bound together and it is ready for casting. Some casts will last for more than one casting but usually not for more than four or five times.

Sand-molds are another medium for casting. A frame consisting of two halves is used. A pattern (made of metal, plastic, wood, paper, or wax) is set in the sand. Parting powder is sifted over it to insure against sticking. More sand is added to cover the pattern and firmly packed down. The top half is removed, then the pattern, leaving an impression in the sand. A sprue is carefully cut from the outside edge to the impression, and then the top half of the frame is put in place and clamped down. Molten metal is poured into the sprue. After cooling, the clamps are removed and the sand is knocked out of the frames with a mallet. The cast pattern is removed, ready for clean-up work.

A more modern form of casting is the lost-wax method. A pattern is usually made out of wax with a sprue attached. The sprued pattern is then set into a casting flask. Investment (a mixture resembling plaster of paris) is poured into the flask, then vibrated to remove the air bubbles. The investment is heated in a furnace to around 1000°F causing the wax pattern to "burn out," leaving a hollow impression where the design once was. The investment mold is then cooled slightly, depending on the type of metal being used, and is ready for casting. Investment molds utilize gravity or centrifugal casting as a means of "pulling" the molten metal into the cavities. Two types of machines are used for this job.

First, a centrifugal casting machine works a simple principle. The machine has a cross-arm that can be wound up much like the propeller of a rubber band airplane. The arm is locked into position and then the cooled investment mold is

Morenci turquoise necklace, $650.00. Courtesy of Treasure Trails Inc., Disneyland Plaza, Ca.

Very unusual Zuni bracelet with round and tear drop cut turquoise. Ring also of Zuni design $500.00. Color of Turquoise Teepee, Lido Village, Newport Beach, Ca.

GENUINE TURQUOISE SPECIMENS ROUGH AND POLISHED
Other Minerals that are often mistaken for Turquoise
Imitation Turquoise, sometimes misleading if not familiar with Genuine Turquoise

BISBEE – TURQUOISE	KINGS TURQUOISE	BLUE GEM TURQUOISE
Mined near Bisbee, Arizona	Mined near Manassa, Colorado	Mined near Battle Mountain, Nevada
MORENCI TURQUOISE	VILLAGROVE TURQUOISE	NO. 8 SPIDER WEBB TURQUOISE
Mined near Morenci, Arizona	Mined near Salida, Colorado	Mined near Tenabo, Nevada
KINGMAN TURQUOISE	CRIPPLE CREEK TURQUOISE	LONE MOUNTAIN TURQUOISE
Mined near Kingman, Arizona	Mined near Colorado Springs, Colorado	Mined near Tonopah, Nevada
SLEEPING BEAUTY TURQUOISE	NEW MEXICO TURQUOISE	FOX MINE TURQUOISE
Mined near Globe, Arizona	Mined near Silver City, New Mexico	Mined near Austin, Nevada
MEXICO OR EVANS TURQUOISE	PERSIAN TURQUOISE	ROYAL BLUE TURQUOISE
Mined near Baja, California	Mined in Persia	Mined near Tonopah, Nevada
TREATED TURQUOISE	HILLSIDE TURQUOISE	STENICH TURQUOISE
Before Treated After Treated Mined near Kingman, Arizona	Mined near Battle Mountain, Nevada	Mined near Tenabo, Nevada

Samples of various nuggets and the finished polished turquoise.

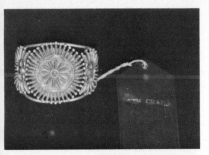

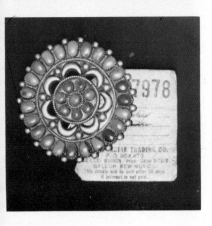

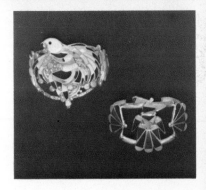

Reading clockwise from upper left: 1. Three Navajo pendants. Center of picture is modern design that younger silversmiths are into — $100.00 to $150.00. 2. Bracelet and ring by the Singer Brothers in Holbrook, Arizona showing style of metric inlay that they presented in the late '60's which has become very popular. It is being copied by North Arizona Indians. Large bracelet is a rare deer design — $100.00 to $300.00. 3. Two bracelets of typical Navajo design. The large round stone is Blue gem turquoise, with a large piece of mother rock in the center. The triangular is a very clear piece of Kingruan turquoise — $300.00. 4. Two typical Zuni inlaid bracelets — $400.00 each. 5. Old pawn Zuni brooch with original pawn ticket dated 1936 showing pawn price of $3.00. Today's value is $200.00. 6. Prize winning Zuni needlepoint bracelet with great detail of silver work. Excellent Morenci turquoise — $750.00. Turquoise Teepee, Lido Village, Newport Beach, Ca.

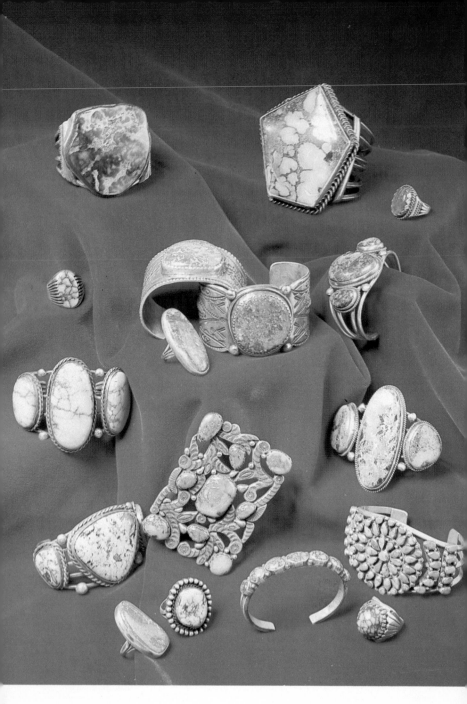

A stunning example of various "Blue Gold" creations. Photo courtesy of Manley Photo-Tucson, Arizona.

put in its place on the machine. Molten metal is poured into the sprue and then the arm is released causing a rapid spinning action. This centrifugal force pulls the metal into the mold, filling the cavities.

The second type of machine used is a vacuum pump. The process is as simple as its name indicates. The investment mold is set on the vacuum pump and the molten metal is poured into the sprue. The machine is turned on and the suction force of the vacuum pulls the metal into the mold.

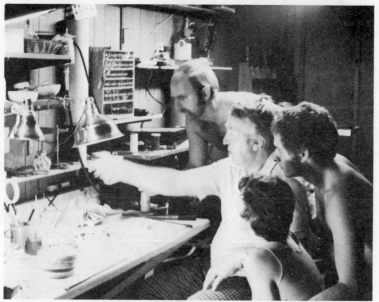

Fritz Wright showing his finished jewelry to friends.

Lost wax casting is a rather expensive means of casting as a great deal of special, expensive equipment is needed.

But casting in general, can be done inexpensively and is a very rewarding experience.

Zuni Squash Blossom necklace with matching earrings and ring. The turquoise is a very clear deep blue Bisbee. Cluster type $1800.00, Treasure Trails Inc., Disneyland Hotel Plaza.

CONCLUSION

Turquoise is now worn by both men and women. Courtesy of Treasure Trails Inc. Disneyland Plaza.

From the Near and Far East to the great American Southwest, from the courts of the Pharoahs to the drawing rooms of Beverly Hills, turquoise has been valued by peoples throughout history as a gemstone of uncommon beauty possessing supernatural powers to protect the wearer from harm or injury and to insure good fortune and prosperity. We have heard how different peoples at different times throughout the ages have ascribed to turquoise such diverse powers as the ability to cure epilepsy, internal ulcerations, and all diseases of the head and heart; to protect the eyes and improve sight; to protect the wearer against falls and injury; to preserve one from harm by one's enemies; to provide immunity to the scorpions' sting and other poisonous

Left to right – Navajo style, coral and turquoise inlay signed A.J. Alfred Joe, narrow inlay bracelet $85.00 retail, Navajo style Winslow, Arizona $240.00 retail, Hopi bracelet $180.00, $260.00 retail turquoise inlay signed A.J. Alfred Joe, Navajo Winslow, Arizona, $180.00 retail coral and turquoise signed A.J. Alfred Joe, Winslow, Arizona.

reptiles; to produce rain; to reconcile man and wife and even to induce hilarity. It is small wonder then that this beautiful gemstone with its colorful history and lore, enhanced by the exquisite jewelry-making techniques of the Southwest Indians, should be enjoying another resurgence in popularity and value.

From left to right – Navajo rope bracelet $140.00 retail, mans Navajo shadow box bracelet 2-stone $240.00 retail, 3-stone Navajo bracelet retail $160.00, Hopi bracelet $180.00 retail, mans Navajo 1-stone bracelet $200.00 retail, 2-stone mans bracelet Navajo $160.00 retail. Courtesy of Hozuna Traders.

The marketing of turquoise has become a very profitable business within the last few years. Since it is in so much demand, many stores such as department stores and small dress shops now carry a turquoise jewelry display.

Gift shops in museums and vacation resorts almost always have turquoise jewelry for sale.

From left to right — already described in another picture. From left to right — Inlay Navajo watchbands signed A.J. Alfred Joe Winslow, Arizona. Retail $90.00, already described in another picture, Navajo 2 stone leaf signed A.J. Alfred Joe, bracelet cluster Navajo- mans $250.00 retail, Sunburst sandcast $160.00 retail, sandcast bracelet 1 stone $120.00 retail, Navajo ring $48.00 retail, heavey shank leaf ring $150.00 retail, wide shank mans rings both $60.00 retail. Courtesy of Hozuna Traders.

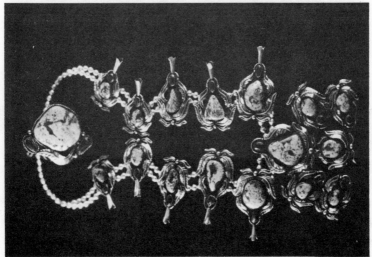

Matched Squash Blossom Necklace and Bracelet Set $3000.00 Retail, courtesy of Hozuna Traders.

Craft shows and swap meets usually have a booth or two filled with turquoise. If you are in search of a bargain it may be found there, but be careful of fakes.

Bearclaw Necklace coral and turquoise (Navajo) $1200.00 retail.

If you are looking for quality and authentic Indian crafted jewelry, there are many stores in your local area. Usually they advertise in the telephone directory or in newspapers. A reputable business is the best source of information and guidance for a novice buyer. Whereas the best turquoise used to be available in Arizona and New Mexico near the source, it is now found in better shops everywhere. (Many Indian owned and operated stores right on the reservations have an overwhelming selection of goods.)

Gallup, New Mexico, is the site for an annual event for the Inter-Tribal Indian Ceremonies. It's usually held in August and is a most festive occasion with a beautiful display of individual tribal costumes and dances. It's an interesting way to spend a few days while looking for turquoise pieces. Dates and information may be obtained from Ceremonial Association, Box 1029, Gallup, New Mexico, 87301.

Mr. De Castro showing author his private collection.

Private showings are another means of quality buying. Many Indian jewelry stores, as well as individuals, hold displays and sales in a private party's home where interested buyers are invited.

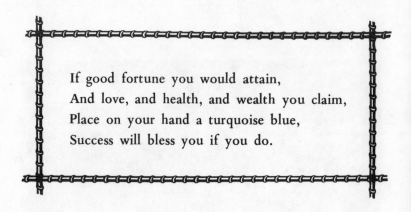

If good fortune you would attain,
And love, and health, and wealth you claim,
Place on your hand a turquoise blue,
Success will bless you if you do.

Suggested Reading

Van Nostrand's Standard Catalog of Gems
    By John Sinkankas — University of Calif.
    Certified Gemologist — American Gem Society
    American Book Co. 1968
    Van Nostrand-Reinhold Co. Publisher
The Navajo and Pueblo Silversmiths
    By John Adair Norman Oklahoma
    University of Oklahoma Press 1966
The Story of Jewelry
    By Marcus Baerwald and Tom Mahoney
    Abelard-Schuman. London, New York 1960
Revised Lapidary Handbook
    By J. Harry Howard
    Howard Greenville, South Carolina 1946
American Gem Trails
    By Richard M. Pearl
    Department of Geology
    Colorado College, Colorado Springs, Colorado
    McGraw-Hill 1964
Turquoise Jewelry of the Indians of the Southwest
    Edna Mae and John Bennett
    Turquoise Books, Colorado
Gemcraft: How to Cut and Polish Gems
    By Lelande Quick and Hugh Leiper, F.G.A.
    Chilton Book Co., Philadelphia 1959
Gemstones to Jewelry
    By James B.
    K.G. Murry Publishing 1967
    Sydney, Australia
Contemporary Jewelry, A Studio Handbook
    By Philip Morton
    Holt, Rinehart and Winston, Inc.
    New York
Handbook of Lost Wax and Investment Casting
    By James E. Sopcak
Turquois
    By Joseph E. Pogue The Rio Grande Press, Inc.
    Glorieta, New Mexico 87535

INDIAN AND TURQUOISE SHOW
39000 PEOPLE VISITED THERE TO BUY
AND SHOP FOR TURQUOISE
IN OCTOBER OF 1974

Books Published by Main Street Press
P.O. Box 4262
Anaheim, California 92803

CALIFORNIA GHOST TOWN TRAILS By A.L. Abbott (Revised)
* Factual information on ghost towns. 78 pages, paperback.
* 36 photographs showing some of the old towns as they appear today, not as they did 50 or 100 years ago.
* 36 maps with detailed mileage to ghost towns shown to the tenth of a mile.
* Interesting and historical data.
* Much needed and in demand by all rockhounds, treasure hunters, bottle hunters, tourists, and western lore enthusiasts.
* Retail price $2.95.

GEM TRAILS IN CALIFORNIA By A.L. Abbott
* Gem Locations – Mineral locations. 84 pages, paperback.
* 79 detailed maps – Exact mileage to the tenth of a mile.
* 65 actual photos – Locations pin-pointed on the photos and maps.
* 158 places to collect.
* In demand by experienced as well as amateur rockhounds.
* Retail price $2.95.

FUN TRIPS IN SOUTHERN CALIFORNIA By A.L. Abbott
* Fun places to visit in Southern California. 84 pages, paperback.
* 1 & 2 day trips from Los Angeles.
* Where to go, what to do, what to see.
* Where to stay, where to camp.
* Nevada to the coast, San Francisco to Mexico.
* Retail price $2.95.

NEVADA GHOST TOWN TRAILS By A.L. Abbott (Revised Edition)
* Factual information on ghost towns in Nevada. 80 pages, paperback.
* 39 photographs showing some of the old towns as they appear today, not as they did 50 or 100 years ago.
* 34 maps with detailed mileage to ghost towns shown to the tenth of a mile.
* Interesting and historical data.
* Much needed and in demand by all rockhounds, treasure hunters, bottle hunters, tourists, and western lore enthusiasts.
* Retail price $2.95.

OLD BOTTLES – HOW AND WHERE TO FIND THEM By A.L. Abbott
* Not just a catalog or pricing guide like most bottle books, but descriptive information on how and where to find them. 74 pages, paperback.
* Large chapter on identification.
* Handy dating guide enables reader to determine the date of manufacture easily.
* Large chapter of safety and survival to help the bottle hunter return home safely.
* Retail price $2.95.

**Distributed
by
Gem Guides Book Co.
5409 Lenvale
Whittier, Calif. 90601**

Index